This book belongs to:

Florence H

Birthday: march   Age: 6

My favourite
Rainbow Magic fairy is:

polly the party fair

Stick a smiley photo of yourself in
this flower or draw a self-portrait:

ORCHARD BOOKS
338 Euston Road, London NW1 3BH
Orchard Books Australia
Level 17/207 Kent Street, Sydney, NSW 2000

First published in 2008 by Orchard Books.

A CIP catalogue record for this book is available
from the British Library.

ISBN 978 1 40830 272 9

1 3 5 7 9 10 8 6 4 2

Printed in Italy
Orchard Books is a division of Hachette Children's Books,
an Hachette Livre UK company

www.hachettelivre.co.uk

Annual
2009

Take care of this book,
it's fizzing with fairy
fun and sparkles!

Contents

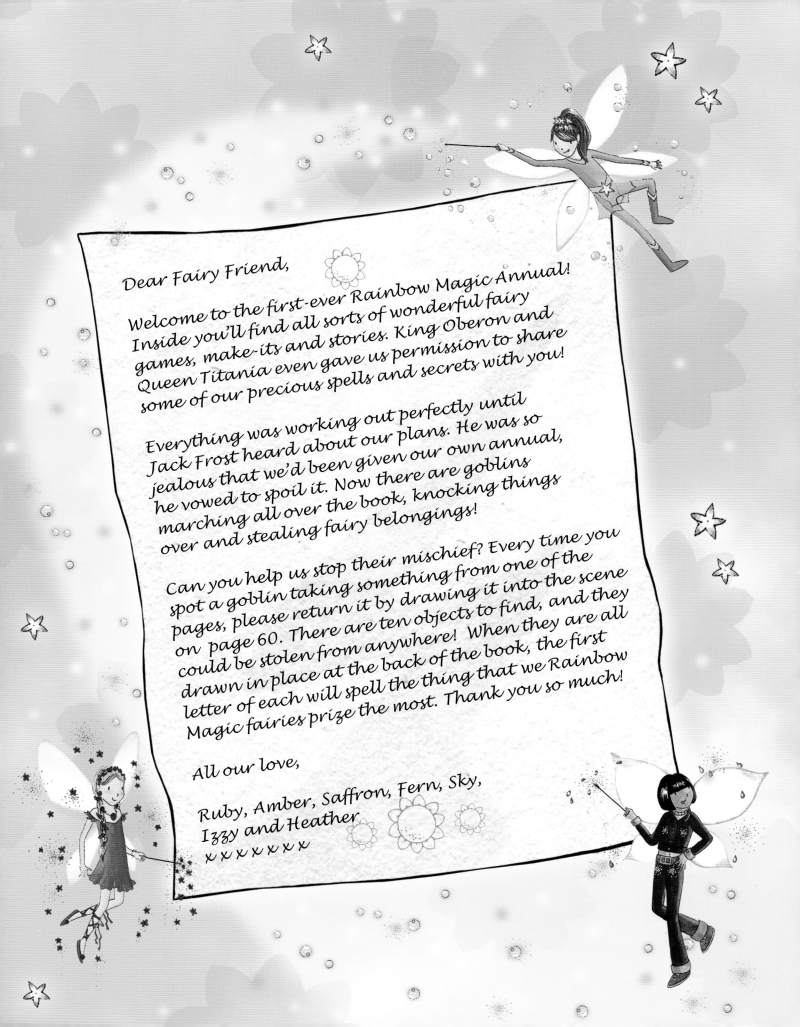

Dear Fairy Friend,

Welcome to the first-ever Rainbow Magic Annual! Inside you'll find all sorts of wonderful fairy games, make-its and stories. King Oberon and Queen Titania even gave us permission to share some of our precious spells and secrets with you!

Everything was working out perfectly until Jack Frost heard about our plans. He was so jealous that we'd been given our own annual, he vowed to spoil it. Now there are goblins marching all over the book, knocking things over and stealing fairy belongings!

Can you help us stop their mischief? Every time you spot a goblin taking something from one of the pages, please return it by drawing it into the scene on page 60. There are ten objects to find, and they could be stolen from anywhere! When they are all drawn in place at the back of the book, the first letter of each will spell the thing that we Rainbow Magic fairies prize the most. Thank you so much!

All our love,

Ruby, Amber, Saffron, Fern, Sky, Izzy and Heather
x x x x x x x

Fairy Favourites

What's the best thing about being a fairy? Is it casting spells and wishes, attending Fairyland banquets, or fluttering through clouds and sliding down rainbows? Use this quiz to discover what you'd like best if you could be a Rainbow Magic fairy for a day.

1. You've just arrived at a birthday party! Do you...

a. Make a beeline for your best friend?
b. Start the dancing off by twirling across the room?
c. Find a mirror to check your party dress looks just right?
d. Put your hand up straightaway to lead the first game?

2. Pick your favourite school subject from the list below.

a. Creative writing.
b. Drama.
c. Art.
d. PE.

3. Where would you rather go on holiday?

a. A quiet cottage in Cornwall.
b. A big group holiday somewhere hot.
c. A Paris city break.
d. The theme parks of Florida.

4. Which of these things would you be most likely to do?

a. Enter a poetry competition.
b. Organise a surprise party.
c. Put together a fancy-dress outfit.
d. Take trampolining lessons.

5. Which of these possessions is the most precious to you?

a. Your latest book.
b. Your photo album.
c. Your sparkly hair bands.
d. Your bike.

Mostly a's

Whispers of magical things

You're a shy girl on the outside, but inside your wonderful imagination is sparkling with fairy spells and wishes. You'd love to be a Rainbow Magic fairy with your own special wand and magic dust to sprinkle.

Mostly b's

A fairy for special occasions

Top of everyone's invitation list, you adore the thought of shrinking down to fairy-size and attending the Fairyland Midsummer Ball! You'd be such a sociable guest, starting off all kinds of tinkly fairy giggles!

Mostly c's

Tiny toes and fairy frocks

Your notebooks are full of scribbles of shimmery frocks, silk slippers and sparkly tiaras. A true follower of fashion, you'd love to swap outfits and accessories with each of the Rainbow Magic fairies.

Mostly d's

There she flutters

Kirsty and Rachel have such adventures each time they get to fly with the Rainbow Magic fairies – you'd like to try it too! An active girl like you will be loop-the-looping in no time!

Meet Ruby the Red Fairy

Ruby the Red Fairy is extra-special as she's the first fairy that Kirsty and Rachel ever met on Rainspell Island!

I'll never forget the day the girls rescued me from the pot at the end of the rainbow!

Happiest hobby
Flying as fast as she can over Fairyland, performing tricks and tumbles.

Personality
Feisty, high-spirited and full of fun.

Fairy playmates
The Dance Fairies and the Sporty Fairies.

Favourite colour
Bright red, the colour of courage and energy.

Yummiest food
Raspberry jelly and strawberry milkshake.

Although she is lighter than a butterfly, Ruby will do anything and go anywhere to help a friend in trouble!

Fairy outfit
Ruby's beautiful dress is the colour of fresh strawberries. She plaits her golden hair with tiny red rose buds and pops crimson slippers on her feet. Her little earrings and locket were a present from Queen Titania.

9

The Pot at the End of the Rainbow

When a stunning rainbow arched over their holiday cottages, Kirsty and Rachel set out to follow it. But instead of a pot of gold at the end of the trail, they discovered something far better – a tiny Rainbow Magic fairy! The poor little creature had been trapped underneath an old black cooking pot. Now that she was free, Ruby the Red Fairy had a very special favour to ask…

"I have six sisters," explained Ruby. "Amber, Saffron, Fern, Sky, Izzy and Heather. It's our job to put all the colours into Fairyland."

"So why were you shut up inside that old pot?" asked Rachel.

Ruby flew into the air, her wings shimmering in the sunshine. Kirsty and Rachel followed her to a pond by a willow tree. Ruby scattered a shower of sparkling fairy dust into the water. "Let me show you what happened yesterday."

The water lit up with a strange, silver light. Rachel and Kirsty watched in astonishment as a picture appeared. A river of the brightest blue ran past hillsides scattered with red and white toadstool houses. At the top of the highest hill stood a palace with four pink towers. Hundreds of fairies and pixies were making their way towards the palace. Everyone seemed very excited.

"Yesterday was the day of the Fairyland Midsummer Ball," Ruby explained. "My sisters and I are in charge of sending out the invitations."

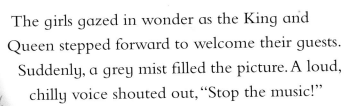

The girls gazed in wonder as the King and Queen stepped forward to welcome their guests. Suddenly, a grey mist filled the picture. A loud, chilly voice shouted out, "Stop the music!"

A tall, bony figure was pushing his way through the crowd. There was ice on his white hair and beard, but his face was screwed up in an angry scowl.

"It's Jack Frost," whispered Ruby.

"We forgot to invite him to the Ball!"

In the pond picture, Queen Titania stepped forward to meet him. "You are very welcome. Please stay and enjoy yourself."

"Too late!" hissed Jack Frost. "You forgot me!"

He pointed a thin, icy finger at the Rainbow Fairies. "My spell will banish the Rainbow Fairies to the seven corners of the mortal world. From this day on, Fairyland will be without colour – for ever!"

Kirsty shivered. "How mean! Why didn't they stop him?"

"Queen Titania couldn't undo his magic completely," said Ruby. "But she used her silver wand to take us to a place where we would be safe."

"Rainspell Island?" asked Rachel.

"That's right," nodded Ruby. "My sisters are somewhere on the Island, too. Will you help me find them and bring the colour back to Fairyland?"

"Of course!" Kirsty and Rachel both cried at once.

"Thank you!" grinned Ruby. "Let's get started right away!"

You can read more about this adventure in *Ruby the Red Fairy* (see pages 62/63 for details).

Flower Fortune Teller

Louise the Lily Fairy loves to hang out with her Petal Fairy friends. Sometimes they take turns reading her pretty water lily fortune teller. Here's how to make your very own!

First collect...

A square sheet of white paper
approx 21cm x 21cm
Paintbrush and paint
Old newspaper
Felt-tip pens

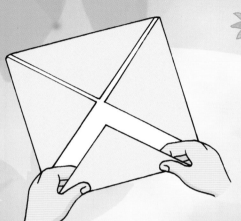

1. Take the square of white paper and paint one side only in your favourite colour. Lay it on some newspaper to dry.

When it's ready, place the square face down and fold each corner into the centre so that the points meet exactly.

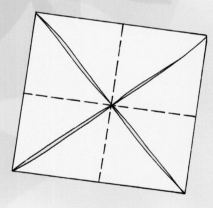

2. Now turn the square over and fold each corner in again.

3. Fold the square in half along the central line, on the side of the fortune teller that has triangles, as shown here in red. Fold it back and forth a few times until a deep crease is formed.

4. Put your thumbs and forefingers into each square on the other side of the fortune teller. Move your fingers up and down and left to right a few times to test the fortune teller out. It's nearly ready!

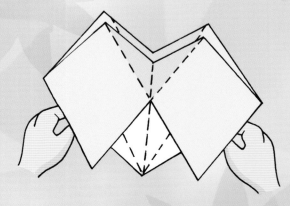

5. Unfold the paper and turn it painted-side down so that you can write on it. Following the diagram below, use felt-tips to write these words, numbers and phrases onto the square.

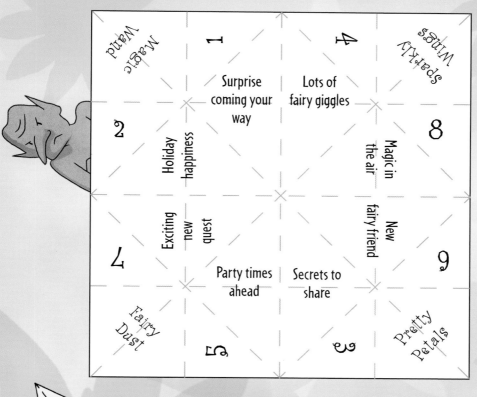

Magic Wand | 1 | 4 | Sparkly Wings
Surprise coming your way | Lots of fairy giggles
2 | Holiday happiness | Magic in the air | 8
Exciting new quest | New fairy friend
7 | Party times ahead | Secrets to share | 9
Fairy Dust | 5 | 3 | Pretty Petals

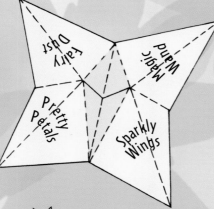

6. Fold your fortune teller back up, following steps 1-4, but with the painted side up. Now find a friend to play with!

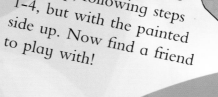

How to play!

❀ Put your thumbs and forefingers under each square and ask your friend to pick her favourite Petal Fairy item.

❀ Spell the item out, opening and closing the fortune teller with each new letter.

❀ Ask your friend to pick a number from the inside. Now lift up the paper and read her magical fairy forecast!

Days Maze

The Fun Day Fairies were so miserable when Jack Frost stole their Fun Day Flags. Can you help Sarah, Thea and all their friends find their way back to the Fairyland Palace? Only the correct route will allow them to pick up the seven missing flags and make the days of the week fun again!

Start

Finish

14

Meet Amber
the Orange Fairy

Amber the Orange Fairy is full of bubbles and fun!

"I love sharing jokes with my Rainbow Magic sisters!"

Personality
Happy-go-lucky, kind and friendly.

Happiest hobby
Making bubbles with her wand!

Favourite colour
Orange, of course!

Fairy playmates
The Jewel Fairies.

Yummiest food
Sweet satsumas and carrot cake.

Only Amber can make the other Rainbow Fairies sparkle with smiles from breakfast to bedtime!

Fairy outfit
Amber's vibrant orange jumpsuit is the height of fairy fashion! She accessorises it with a little chiffon skirt, a chunky belt and her favourite pair of boots.

The Ticklish Seashell

Kirsty and Rachel were running along
Rainspell Island's yellow, sandy beach.
It was the most beautiful day for two new
friends to be on holiday together, but the girls
could only think of one thing – finding another
Rainbow Fairy. Where could the magic be
hiding? Then, just as the girls were heading back
for tea, it happened…

"Stop a second," said Kirsty. "Look over there!"
Suddenly, the sand in front of Kirsty and Rachel
began to drift to one side, as if invisible hands
were pushing it away. A large scallop shell
appeared, pearly white with soft orange streaks.
It was tightly closed.
"Listen!" gasped Rachel. Inside,
a tiny, silvery voice was talking.

Very carefully, Rachel picked up the shell.
"I mustn't be scared," said the tiny voice.
"Help will come soon."
"Is there a fairy in there?" whispered
Kirsty.
"Yes!" cried the voice. "I'm Amber
the Orange Fairy."
Rachel and Kirsty stared at each other.
They'd found the next Rainbow Fairy!
"Quick!" cried Rachel. "Let's get the
shell open." She tried to pull the two halves

Humm m......

of the scallop apart. Nothing happened.

"What's going on?" Amber called.

"We can't open the shell," Kirsty said. "But we'll think of something."

"We could try tapping it on a rock," suggested Rachel.

Kirsty shook her head. "That might hurt Amber."

Suddenly Rachel remembered something. "What about the magic bags the Fairy Queen gave us?"

After the friends had rescued Ruby the Red Fairy, Queen Titania had presented each of them with a bag of magic tools to help their fairy-finding quest.

Rachel peered into her beach bag. Inside, one of the magic bags was glowing with a golden light. Carefully, Rachel lifted it out.

"Open it quickly," whispered Kirsty.

As Rachel undid the bag, a fountain of glittering sparks flew out. She pulled out a shimmering golden feather.

"What shall we do with it?" wondered Kirsty.

From the inside of the shell, Amber laughed. It sounded like the tinkle of a tiny bell. "You tickle the shell, of course!" she said.

Rachel began to tickle the shell with the feather. The friends heard a soft, gritty chuckle. Then another and another. The shell began to open.

"It's working," Kirsty gasped. "Keep tickling, Rachel!"

The shell was laughing harder now. Suddenly Amber the Orange Fairy shot out of the shell and up into the air, turning cartwheels through the sky.

"I'm free!" cried Amber joyfully.

You can read more about this adventure in Amber the Orange Fairy (see pages 62/63 for details).

Let's Draw Ruby!

Draw a fantastic picture of Ruby the Red Fairy, using these pages as a guide. All you need is a piece of paper, a pencil and some felt-tipped pens or colouring pencils. With a little practice, you'll be picture-perfect in no time!

1. First you will need to draw a circle for Ruby's head. Now sketch in some lines to represent the main parts of her body, as shown. You could trace these from this picture.

2. Sketch in the shape of Ruby's pretty dress.

3. Now add the neck, arms and legs. Don't forget to draw in the shapes of her hands and feet!

4. It's time to add the outlines of Ruby's fluttery wings and her magical wand.

5. Draw Ruby's hair and start to add detail to her dress. Begin to sketch out the ribbons on her legs.

6. Now draw Ruby's facial features, arms and hands. Add her necklace, finish sketching her hair and don't forget to complete her pretty ballet pumps and ribbons!

7. Go over the final outline in a black fineliner pen, then rub out the sketch. Now use your felt-tipped pens or colouring pencils to colour your picture and add stars and fairy dust all around Ruby. Well done!

Guide to Story Writing

Begin at the beginning

The best storybooks hook their readers in with a captivating first line. What would your fairytale beginning be? Here's the first sentence from India the Moonstone Fairy book to get you started:

"Kirsty, help!" Rachel Walker shouted. "The goblins are going to get me!"

Keep a Journal

Take the time to jot down your thoughts and feelings every day, even if it is only a line or two. Don't be tempted to flick back until at least a month has passed. When you do, the unfolding events should give you some interesting story ideas.

Meet your heroine

If you are struggling to think of an exciting story, maybe you can picture the sort of character that you would like to write about instead? Describe what she looks like and what her hobbies are. Now try to imagine where you might meet a person like her...

Dream ideas

Keep a notepad on your bedside table — inspiration can strike at any time! If you have an interesting dream, write it down before you go back to sleep.

Twists and turns

The trick to writing a good story is to keep your readers guessing what is going to happen on the next page. Fill your story with surprises — think what the reader would expect to happen next and then write the opposite.

Keep it simple

The Rainbow Magic stories are over 75 pages long, but your stories don't need to have so many words in them! Make sure your story has a strong beginning, middle and end, but don't make it too complicated! The simplest ideas are the best.

Bertram's Big Crossword

The Rainbow Fairies would be lost without their froggy friend Bertram. Only fairy minds sparkle brightly enough to try out his new word grid.

Across

1. Kirsty and Rachel's holiday island (9).
2. Fairyland's magical Queen (7).
3. Storybook land visited by Izzy the Indigo Fairy (7).
4. The name of the yellow Rainbow Fairy (7).
5. Purple jewellery worn by Heather the Violet Fairy (5).

Down

1. Kirsty and Rachel's gifts from the Fairy King and Queen in Ruby the Red Fairy (5,4).
2. Jack Frost's home is made of this (3).
3. Animal that helped save Sky the Blue Fairy (4).
4. Something that every fairy can do (3).

Answers can be found on page 61!

Meet Rachel...

Rachel and Kirsty share the most wonderful secret ever! As well as being best friends, they've shared some amazing adventures with a host of magical fairies.

Name
Rachel Walker.

Age
11 years old.

Home
Tippington Town.

Yummiest food
Fresh fruit salad and iced buns.

Prized pet
Her shaggy dog, Buttons.

Personality
Adventurous, fun-loving and friendly.

Most prized possession
The stunning animal charm bracelet Queen Titania gave her for helping the Pet Keeper Fairies.

Fairy playmates
Rachel loves them all, although she has a soft spot for Ruby the Red Fairy as she's the first fairy they ever helped!

Biggest fairy challenge
Bumping into things! When she's shrunk to fairy-size, Rachel can fly like the wind, but sometimes she forgets to look where she is going.

Most unforgettable adventure
Helping the Party Fairies save King Oberon and Queen Titania's 1000th jubilee celebrations.

Best outfit
The black cat fancy dress that the girls wore to the Sunnydays Carnival. Rachel topped her ebony costume with a velvety eye mask and a fluffy black tail. The friends even drew whiskers on their faces with eyeliner – purr-fect!

...and Kirsty!

Personality
Kind-hearted, resourceful and great at rescuing fairies!

Most prized possession
The glittery snow dome she was presented with after saving the seven Rainbow Fairies.

Fairy playmates
There are so many fab fairies, it's impossible to choose!

Best outfit
The stunning angel costume conjured up by Flora the Fancy Dress Fairy for the masked ball at McKersey Castle. The powdery white dress came with matching feathery wings and a delicate silver halo – heavenly!

Name
Kirsty Tate.

Age
11 years old.

Home
Wetherbury Village.

Yummiest food
Toffee popcorn and her mum's homemade apple pie.

Prized pet
Her kitten, Pearl.

Biggest fairy challenge
Flying. When it's time to flutter her fairy wings, Kirsty can feel nervous. The ground is a long way down when you're smaller than a daisy!

Most unforgettable adventure
Helping Holly the Christmas Fairy get Santa's sleigh back to stop Jack Frost spoiling the holidays for children everywhere.

I Can See a Rainbow!

Everybody knows that something magical happens when a rainbow curves across the sky, but why does it appear? Goldie the Sunshine Fairy and Hayley the Rain Fairy have fluttered in to explain all about these beautiful arches in the clouds...

Have you ever been out on a sunny day, only to find that it's started to pitter-patter with rain? When there's wet weather and sunshine at the same time, you're in luck. There's a chance that you could spot a rainbow!

What is a rainbow?

Sunlight looks white, but it is actually made up of seven colours – red, orange, yellow, green, blue, indigo and violet. When sunbeams shine through raindrops, the white gets split into this fan of shades. The colours bow over the horizon in a layered arch that's beautiful to see. If you look carefully, you might even get to spot a second fainter rainbow, curving outside the arch.

Golden sunshine and mirrored raindrops are such a magical combination!

Doodle's Did You Know...?

- When you look at a rainbow, the sun will always be behind you.

- Rainbows are made up of the complete spectrum of colours. Although we can only see seven stripes in the arch, there are more shades there that our eyes can't see.

- You never know when a rainbow might come, but waterfalls and fountains are especially good places to see reflecting sunshine. Sometimes on the beach, you might also be able to spot rainbow colours shining in the salty spray.

Rainbow myths

What lies at the end of a rainbow – is it really a crock of gold? Or might you be lucky enough to stumble upon a pot of Rainbow Fairies? People have wondered about these beautiful arches for thousands of years. Rainbows have been described as bridges to heaven or even a great necklace of jewels hanging from the clouds!

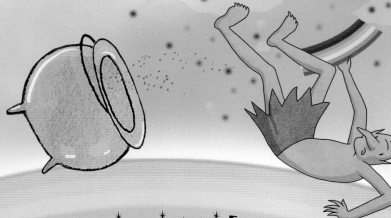

Mysterious moonbows

Have you ever seen a moonbow? Only a handful of people can say they've spotted such an enchanted sight!

Very occasionally, at night-time, the light of the moon is reflected in raindrops. The light of the moon is much weaker than the sun's, so its bows appear as faint white arches glowing in the darkness.

Fairy Fortunes

So much can happen in a fairy year! Answer the questions on this flowchart to discover what 2009 holds for you. Trace your way along the paths until you reach a coloured circle. Then your destiny will be revealed in the same-coloured oval at the bottom of the page.

Start
Do you seek adventure or a happy home?

Adventure
What's best? Holidays or school days?

Happy home
Do you like to look after people or do you prefer to be pampered?

Holidays
Do you like to be muddy or manicured?

School days
Are you a neat freak or a messy miss?

Pampered
What's more fun? A disco or a sleepover?

Carer
Do you keep a secret or shout it out?

Manicured
Do you like chatting or dancing?

Sleepover
Are you into pop or ponies?

Muddy
Would you rather hike mountains or walk the dog?

Neat
Are you a photographer or a diary-keeper?

Messy
Do you like early mornings or a late lie-in?

Disco
Do you prefer fairy cakes or milkshake?

Secret
Are you best at PE or Art?

Shout it out
Do you like surprises or prefer what you know?

Dancing

Diary-keeper

Fairy cakes

Walk the dog

Art

Chatting

Photographer

Late lie-in

PE

Hike mountains

Early mornings

Ponies

What you know

Milkshake

Pop

Surprises

Fabulous friend
You are happiest when you are surrounded by the people that you love the most. Continue to put such thought and care into your friendships and you'll be rewarded with some very special times in 2009. There's even a chance that a brand-new friend could already be close by!

Far-away fairy!
You're a born explorer, blessed with a natural curiosity and an eye for adventure! The next year promises to be crammed with excitement for you, but take note – magical happenings occur in the most unexpected places...

Party girl!
The room lights up when you walk in, you're such a bubbly bundle of fun! You're set to be top of everyone's invitation list in the year ahead, whether it's a barbecue, disco or a birthday tea. You also have a hidden talent – an artistic streak that's second to none.

Animal instincts
You adore all pets and here's a secret from the Pet Keeper Fairies – they adore you too! You are a patient, thoughtful animal-lover who knows just the right way to make creatures feel safe and happy. Your kind ways will get noticed in the months ahead.

Super Spell-Caster

If you believe in fairies with all your heart and promise to use magic only for good, you can cast your own spells! Make up a fairy poem and then whisper it into a breeze at sunset... If you're lucky, your wish may come true.

Wand-waving tip from the top

Before you whisper any spell, point your wand up to the sky (a wand can be made from anything long and pointy!) and then circle it in the air seven times. Sprinkling a thimbleful of glitter will create an extra shimmer of fairy magic.

The Fairyland five

Here's a list of our favourite everyday spells. Which one do you like best?

Birthday spell
Brings a happy day with a cake, candles and lots of special treats!

Warm weather wishes
Perfect for chanting before an outing to the beach or a school sports day.

Get well spell
Smile and whisper this verse near a poorly person and they're bound to feel better!

Good luck charm
Just the thing to write on a piece of paper and give to anyone taking a tricky test or moving schools.

Enchanted friendship wish
A very special spell that only works if it is recited while holding hands with someone you care about.

Rhyme all the time!

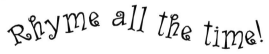

Are you ready to make up a spell?
All Rainbow Magic spells must be gentle,
kind and trip off the tongue in a verse.
Use our fairy rhyme list to get started…

airy / fairy
bean / clean / queen / seen
bell / shell / spell / tell
bend / friend / lend / send
bitter / glitter
bright / excite / flight / fright / height / knight / might / night
care / fair / lair / hair/ scare / share

celebrations / decorations
cool / jewel / pool
dust / gust / must / trust
far / star
fine / time / mine
flower / hour / power / tower
fly / goodbye / high / sigh / sky / why

Sweet Fairy Drinks

Rainbow Magic fairies make a special effort when their friends come to visit. Homemade fizzy pop and fruit smoothies are always offered on warm, sunny days. Why not try one of these magical recipes the next time you have a visitor?

Fairy fizz

This recipe is also known as Champagne Blush in Fairyland, because the pink bubbles can pop on your nose!

- Pour one glass of lemonade and one glass of fresh apple juice into a jug.
- Stir in a few drops of red food colouring, then add some crushed ice.
- Serve in small goblets or pretty wine glasses with a glacé cherry on top.

Strawberries and cream

Ask a grown-up to help you chop up some fresh strawberries until you have filled two tea cups.

- Pour the strawberries into a blender, along with two cups of vanilla ice cream and the same amount of sparkling mineral water.
- Add one tea cup of tinned pineapple chunks and ask an adult to help you blend until you have a smooth, creamy mixture.
- Serve the drink with a straw in tall milkshake glasses – it's fairy heaven!

Petal ice cubes

Ella has a special surprise to make her fruit cocktails look even more scrummy – she pops a rose petal ice cube into every glass!

- Take an ice cube tray and fill it half full of water before freezing.
- Check with an adult first, then carefully pick a few rose petals from the garden that haven't been treated with insect repellent. Wash each petal carefully then blot dry on some kitchen towel.
- Take out your frozen ice cube tray and place a petal on top of each square. Cover with a teaspoon of water and return it to the freezer
- When the tray has frozen again, fill the cubes up to the top and freeze one last time. Pop the crystal-cold cubes out of the tray and float one or two in each glass.

Top tip

It's easy to give the rim of your drinks glasses a sweet sparkly coating. Chill each glass in the fridge for half an hour, then squeeze a little lemon juice around the top. Now carefully dip each one in a saucer of caster sugar – it's magic! Desiccated coconut and chocolate powder make good frostings, too.

Meet Saffron
the Yellow Fairy

Saffron the Yellow Fairy has a heart made of pure gold!

. I was in a sticky situation until Kirsty and Rachel found me and brought me back to my Rainbow Fairy sisters!

Personality
Clever, inventive and sweet-natured.

Happiest hobby
Flying with Queenie and the rest of the bumble bees!

Fairy playmates
The Pet Keeper Fairies.

Favourite colour
Yellow, the shade of summer and bright ideas!

Yummiest food
Fizzy sherbet lemons and corn on the cob.

Saffron's lively mind is full of fantastic facts and figures. Her sisters ask for her wise words about anything and everything!

Fairy outfit
Saffron always dazzles when she wears her bright yellow scoop T-shirt and shorts. Her golden raindrop necklace and sparkly bracelets set off her glowing blonde bob to perfection.

29

Hive Surprise

Now that they had found two Rainbow Fairies, Kirsty and Rachel weren't going to give up until they had rescued all seven – they'd do anything to help put the colours back into Fairyland! One sunny afternoon, Kirsty's mum and dad took the girls for a walk past Mrs Merry's house. Mrs Merry kept bees in her lovely apple orchard, but one hive in particular made the most sweet-tasting honey…

Rachel dipped her finger into the little pool of honey and then popped it into her mouth. She felt a delicious tingle on her tongue. "It tastes all fizzy!" she whispered.

Kirsty's eyes were shining. "Look!"

Rachel saw that the honey was sparkling with a thousand tiny, gold lights. "Where did this honey come from?"

Mrs Merry pointed to the hive underneath the biggest apple tree. "The honey from that one tastes especially good at the moment."

Kirsty grinned at Rachel. "It must be fairy honey!"

Mrs Merry found two beekeeper's hoods in her garden shed. "You're welcome to take a closer look, but you had better put these on."

Rachel and Kirsty pulled the hoods over their heads.

They needed to see inside the hive, but they couldn't look with Mrs Merry watching them. Ruby had warned the girls that no grown-ups should see fairies.

Suddenly Kirsty had an idea. "Mrs Merry, could I have a drink of water, please?"

"Of course you can, dear," the old lady said, disappearing inside the cottage.

As soon as she had gone, the friends carefully lifted the sticky lid off the beehive. Suddenly a shower of sparkling gold dust shot up and out of the hive. Fairy dust!

Rachel peered down into the hive. Inside, a tiny girl was sitting cross-legged on a piece of honeycomb. A bee was resting happily on her lap.

"Oh, Kirsty," Rachel whispered. "We've found another Rainbow Fairy."

"I'm Saffron the Yellow Fairy," the fairy said in a tinkling voice.

Kirsty and Rachel told Saffron how they'd already found two of her sisters. As the fairy listened, another bee crawled out of the honeycomb and buzzed up to her.

"This is my best friend, Queenie," said Saffron. She picked up a tiny comb and began to groom the bee's silky hair.

Kirsty and Rachel looked at each other in dismay.

"Saffron, you can't stay here," burst out Kirsty. "We need all the Rainbow sisters if Fairyland is ever to get its colours back!"

Saffron picked up her wand and jumped to her feet. "Yes, of course!"

Just then, Rachel shivered as something cold brushed against her cheek. It was a snowflake in the middle of summer!

"We'd better hurry," she said. "Jack Frost's goblins must be near..."

You can read more about this adventure in *Saffron the Yellow Fairy* (see pages 62/63 for details).

Meet Jack Frost and the Goblins

Jack Frost has an army of naughty goblins to help him create chaos. Whenever there's a chill in the air, the fairies must be on their guard...

I will have my revenge for not being invited to the Fairyland Midsummer Ball!

Name
Jack Frost.

Favourite colour
Ice-white.

Personality
Cold-hearted, jealous and mean.

Home
His turreted frozen Ice Castle.

Frosty friends
Only his band of grumpy goblin servants.

Most trusted magic
His powerful banishment spell.

Frosty Features
A chill breeze always swirls around Jack's bony figure and angry face. His ice-blue robes are trimmed with sharp icicles. Frost glints in his white hair and beard. His pointy elf boots leave icy footprints behind him.

Horrible hobby
Jack thinks he's a magnificent artist. He's always etching frozen designs on window panes, but the fact that no one ever seems to notice them never fails to put him in a frosty mood.

Name
The Goblins.

Personality
Selfish, sneaky but very dim.

Home
The dungeons of Jack Frost's Ice Castle.

Favourite food
Goblins are so greedy they'll eat anything, even dog food!

Horrible hobby
Taking fairy possessions and trampling on flowers.

Frosty friends
None. Most goblins even fight amongst themselves.

Worst time of year
Unfortunately it's winter. Jack Frost gives them lots of jobs to do and goblins hate having cold feet!

Frosty features
The tallest goblins are as high as Kirsty and Rachel's waists, but Jack Frost often uses his powers to make them taller or smaller! All goblins are ugly green creatures with big feet and sharp pointy ears and noses.

We're always ready to cause mischief!

How to be a Good Fairy

Grace the Glitter Fairy has waved her sparkly wand over this page to present you with the ten promises in the Rainbow Magic code. Are you ready to whisper these wise fairy words?

Be kind to everyone

Even frosty folk can melt when they're greeted with a friendly face and a smile.

Spread the magic

Write spells, sing songs and make wands to wave. Fairies love tiaras, wings and anything sparkly!

Put friends first

Always be there for any friend who needs you, and they'll be there for you.

Look after animals

Animals can see fairies too! Be kind to pets and respect animals of all shapes and sizes.

Little things mean a lot

A home-made birthday gift, a tiny note or a thoughtful phone call can show just how much you care.

Everyone's invited!

Rainbow Fairies always play and work as a team. It's surprising what you can do if you stick together!

Be happy to help

Always volunteer before you are asked and your acts of friendship will never be forgotten.

Laugh, play and celebrate

Never let a birthday or special occasion pass you by!

See the beauty in nature

Look closely and you'll discover that the sparkling dew on the morning grass is actually thousands of tiny diamonds scattered by a Jewel Fairy.

Rainbow Magic is all around!

Never forget that Rainbow Magic is the magic shimmering inside you. Believe in yourself and no obstacle will ever be able to stand in your way.

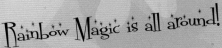

Meet Fern the Green Fairy

Fern the Green Fairy's nut-brown bunches and leafy wand conjure up all the wonder of the forest!

I love fluttering through the trees to say hello to each of my woodland friends!

Happiest hobby
Growing flower seeds in little pots.

Personality
Hopeful, caring and courageous.

Favourite colour
Green, the colour of spring!

Fairy playmates
The Petal Fairies.

Yummiest food
Shiny apples and veggies with guacamole dip.

Fern's favourite spell is her extra-fast growing spell!

Fairy outfit
Fern's vibrant green top and fitted trousers are decorated with pretty leaf shapes at the waist, neck and ankles. Her tiny earrings and pendant glint in the sunlight, and match her emerald wand perfectly!

A Fluffy Escape

Kirsty and Rachel were thrilled to discover Fern the Green Fairy in a garden maze, but an icy breeze in the air warned them that goblins weren't far behind! Fern used her magic to shrink the girls to fairy-size so that they could hide in the branches of a tree. While the goblins stomped towards them, Fern found just the friend to help them get back to the pot at the end of the rainbow…

"Hello," Fern called softly. Rachel and Kirsty turned to look.

A furry, grey face was peeping shyly round the tree trunk. It was a squirrel.

"Maybe he'd like a hazelnut?" suggested Kirsty.

There was a big, shiny nut growing right next to her. Rachel, Fern and Kirsty all tugged at the nut until it came off the branch with a jump.

"What's your name?" asked Fern, holding the nut out to the squirrel.

The squirrel gently took the hazelnut and held it in his front paws.

"I'm Fluffy," squeaked the squirrel, between nibbles.

"I'm Fern," said the fairy. "Will you help us get away from the goblins?"

Fluffy shivered. "I don't like goblins."

"We won't let them hurt you," Fern promised. "Can you give us a ride?"

Fluffy nodded. Rachel, Kirsty and Fern climbed onto the squirrel's back. It was just like sinking into a big, soft blanket.

"Let's go, Fluffy!" cried Fern.

Kirsty and Rachel held on tightly as the squirrel jumped out of the tree, right over the goblins' heads! He landed neatly on the nearest hedge.

Fern leaned forwards to whisper in Fluffy's ear.

"Well done. Now, the next one!"

The squirrel moved so fast, they soon reached the edge of the maze.

"Which way do we go now, girls?" asked Fern.

Rachel and Kirsty looked blank.

"This isn't the way we came in," explained Rachel.

"Oh!" Kirsty had an idea. "What about looking in our magic bags?"

Queen Titania had given them a bag each, for whenever they needed help.

Kirsty opened her bag and looked inside. One of the bags was glowing with a silvery light. She pulled out a thin, green tube, covered with sparkling gold stars.

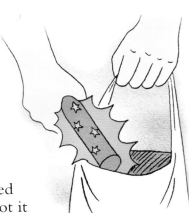

"It looks like a firework," Rachel said.

"It's a fairy firework!" cried Fern excitedly. "We can shoot it into the sky, and my sisters will see it from the pot. Then they'll know we need help."

Kirsty stood the firework firmly in a patch of earth, then she and Rachel moved away from it. Fern softly touched the top with her wand.

Suddenly the firework shot upwards, bursting in a shower of emerald stars.

The girls held their breath.

Where would this adventure take them now?

You can read more about this adventure in *Fern the Green Fairy* (see pages 62/63 for details).

Petal Power!

Growing flowers is such a rewarding thing to do. Sunflowers, with their sunny yellow faces, always make Charlotte the Sunflower Fairy smile! Plant seeds in little pots on your windowsill, then give them to your friends instead of party bags!

First collect...

Empty yoghurt pots
Poster paint
Paint brush
Stickers or ribbon

Compost
Sunflower seeds
Plastic food bags
Lolly sticks
Felt-tip pens

1 Cover the yoghurt pots with brightly-coloured poster paint. Stand the pots upside down to dry.

2 Decorate the pots with cute stickers, or tie a ribbon round them in a bow.

3 Fill each pot with compost and make a hole with your thumb about 2cm deep.

4 Pop one seed into the hole and cover it with compost. Sprinkle a little water on the top.

5 Carefully put the pots into clear plastic food bags and seal them up. This will help the seeds stay warm. Store your pots in a dry, dark place.

6 When the first leaves begin to bud, remove the bags and put the pots on a sunny windowsill. Don't forget to give them a little water every day.

7 Write each of your guests' names on a wooden lolly stick and push them into the pots. Your gifts are ready to be handed out!

Don't forget to tell your friends to look after their seedlings! When the plants reach 10cm tall they can be planted out in the garden. Which one of you can grow the tallest flower?

Magical Mottos

Chrissie the Wish Fairy has used her strongest magic to create four precious mottos for you. Using the fairy picture code below, decipher each magical phrase. You can even create your own mottos using this picture code!

A = ♥	H = ✳	O = ✿	V = wand
B = flower	I = gem	P = lightning	W = cloud
C = bee	J = drop	Q = crystal	X = bubbles
D = diamond	K = cupcake	R = cherry	Y = wings
E = star	L = frog	S = butterfly	Z = bow
F = mushroom	M = moon	T = cloud	
G = castle	N = balloon	U = note	

1 _F_ _R_ _I_ _E_ _N_ _D_ _S_   _F_ _O_ _R_ _E_ _V_ _E_ _R_

2 _S_ _M_ _I_ _L_ _E_ _S_   _A_ _N_ _D_   _H_ _U_ _G_ _S_

_F_ _O_ _R_   _Y_ _O_ _U_

3 _D_ _R_ _E_ _A_ _M_ _S_   _D_ _O_   _C_ _O_ _M_ _E_   _T_ _R_ _U_ _E_

Create Your Own Story

Now it's your chance to create your own Rainbow Magic story! Why did Queen Titania and King Oberon summon the fairies to them? Use your storytelling and drawing skills to bring the tale to life.

Characters

Will you introduce a brand new fairy or draw some of your favourites? If you're stuck, choose one from this list…

Danielle the Daisy Fairy

Jasmine the Present Fairy

Chloe the Topaz Fairy

Melodie the Music Fairy

Bethany the Ballet Fairy

Thea the Thursday Fairy

Thank you for coming so quickly, dear Fairies.

We have a special reason for summoning you to the palace today.

1

2

5

6

Wonderful Words

Not sure what to write in your speech bubbles? These words should help you conjure up some Fairyland magic...

Getting around

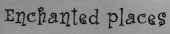

whizz	skip
glide	somersault
flutter	twirl
pirouette	dash

Enchanted places

toadstool ring
secret passageway
waterfalls
flower garden

Curious creatures

elf	leprechaun
goblin	pixie
sprite	dragon
unicorn	dwarf

Magical happenings

sparkle	twinkle
shimmer	glisten
glitter	glow

3

4

7

8

Riding on Rainbows

Sometimes, on the way back from Fairyland, the fairies conjure up a special rainbow for Rachel and Kirsty to ride home! Use felt-tips or colouring pencils and the colour key to bring the picture to life.

Colour Key

red	1	indigo	6
orange	2	violet	7
yellow	3	brown	8
green	4	pink	9
blue	5		

Meet Sky
the Blue Fairy

Sky the Blue Fairy was pale and poorly until Kirsty and Rachel fished her out of her rock-pool prison!

My wand creates blueberry-scented stars whenever I'm happy!

Personality
Imaginative, patient and artistic.

Happiest hobby
Painting hazy pictures in the clouds that everyone enjoys!

Fairy playmates
The Weather Fairies.

Favourite colour
Blue, the colour of creativity and calm.

Yummiest food
Blueberry muffins!

Sky the Blue Fairy has a knack of making anywhere feel comfy, cosy and utterly magical!

Fairy outfit
Sky likes to wear a dress the colour of bluebells with delicate silver sleevelets and a matching choker. She sets her blonde curls off with a crystal tiara and the tiniest star earrings.

Sky's Fairy Friendship Ring

Rachel and Kirsty had tried so hard to warm Sky up, but nothing was working. They'd found the poor shivering Blue Fairy trapped in a frozen rock pool on the beach. The girls watched as she lay on a rock, her colour draining away. A friendly bunch of crabs had even tried to warm her up with seagull feathers, but Sky still didn't have the strength to fly…

"My poor wings," said Sky, her eyes filling with tears.

Kirsty and Rachel glanced at each other. The goblins had got closer to Sky than any of the other Rainbow Fairies.

And now the Blue Fairy was hardly blue at all!

"Let me carry you," offered Rachel. "We'll take you to your sisters."

She cupped her hands and scooped up the feather nest with the fairy inside.

As soon as the girls walked into the glade where the pot at the end of the rainbow was hidden, all the Rainbow Fairies clustered round Sky. As Rachel put Sky down beside the pot, a large green frog hopped out.

"Miss Sky!" croaked Bertram, King Oberon's footman.

The fairy didn't answer. Her eyes started to close. She was so pale, her arms and legs seemed almost transparent.

Bertram looked serious. "I think it's time for you all to try a spell."

Amber frowned. "It might not work with only four of us. Rainbow Magic needs seven fairies." Apart from her and Sky, Kirsty and Rachel had only found Ruby, Saffron and Fern.

"We have to try," Ruby said. "Quick, let's make a fairy ring."

The Rainbow Fairies fluttered into a circle above Sky. Ruby lifted her wand and chanted:

"In a fairy ring we fly,
To bring blue colour back to Sky!"

The fairies waved their wands. Four different colours of dust sparkled in the air – red, orange, yellow and green. The dust covered Sky in a glittering cloud.

"Something's happening!" cried Kirsty. She could see that Sky's short dress and boots were turning bluer and bluer.

Whoosh!

A shimmering cloud of sapphire stars sprinkled down on them.

"We did it!" cried Amber, turning a cartwheel in the air.

Sky yawned and sat up. She brushed the feathers away and looked down at herself. Her face lit up. Her dress was blue again!

"My wings feel strong enough to fly now," she said.

She flapped them twice, then zoomed into the air to hug her sisters.

Rachel and Kirsty smiled at each other in relief. They only had two days left to find the remaining missing fairies before the end of their holiday!

You can read more about this adventure in *Sky the Blue Fairy* (see pages 62/63 for details).

45

Fairy Fashion

Rainbow Magic fairies love dressing up! There are no rules in fairy fashion – all you have to do is choose a look that brings out the natural beauty shining inside you.

What's your true fairy-style? Try this quiz to find out – work down from top to toe, picking the item that you like best each time.

Headwear

a. Over-sized cap worn to one side.
b. Sparkly tiara.
c. Hair comb decorated with roses.
d. Beret with little badges pinned on.

Tops

a. Vest top in a bright colour.
b. Shiny halter-neck.
c. Ruffled wrap-top.
d. Stripy scoop-neck.

Skirts, Dresses and Trousers

a. Cargo trousers.
b. Puff-ball mini with leggings.
c. Long, layered skirt stitched with tingly bells.
d. Vintage prom dress.

Shoes

a. Funky trainers with wheelie heels.
b. Trendy knee-high boots.
c. Roman-style sandals.
d. Cute buckled Mary-Janes.

Accessories

a. Chunky belt.
b. Clutch bag decorated with sequins.
c. Masses of big, gold bangles.
d. Heart-shaped sunglasses.

Mostly a's

You're the true queen of casual, happiest in trousers and unfussy tops! Pumps, cropped jeans, funky tees and gingham shirts would all work well with your chilled-out style!

Mostly b's

You're the ultimate glamour puss, a trendy party girl who dresses to impress. You like to see a new look every time you step in front of your bedroom mirror!

Mostly c's

Your bold style is eye-catching, colourful and full of fun. You look sensational in ra-ra skirts, threaded gypsy tops and embroidered denim.

Mostly d's

You are the princess of vintage! Your ability to mix and match old and new clothes gives you a signature style that is all your very own.

DIY Fashion Designer

Using your imagination, can you create a fabulous new look for this Rainbow Magic fairy? Design her main outfit and then add items such as tiaras, hair decorations and jewellery. The boxes dotted around the page should give you inspiration for those essential finishing touches!

Belts

Shoes

Jewellery

Hair accessories

Fairy Cakes

This is Cherry the Cake Fairy's favourite birthday cupcake recipe, straight from her Fairyland kitchen! Pop on an apron, make a batch and then sprinkle on your own toppings and decorations. These fairy cakes look lovely when they are piled into a multi-coloured stack and then dotted with candles.

First collect...

125g soft margarine
125g caster sugar
1 teaspoon vanilla extract
2 large eggs
125g self-raising flour
12 pretty paper cake cases
100g icing sugar
Food colouring
Cake decorations

1 Ask a grown-up to heat the oven to 180°C, Gas Mark 4 or 360°F. Set 12 cake cases out on a baking tray.

2

2 Put the margarine and sugar together in a mixing bowl and cream together with the back of a fork.

3 When the mixture is smooth and a pale yellow colour, add the vanilla extract. Now beat in the eggs and add the flour a little at a time.

3

4 Gently spoon some cake mix into each of the cases and bake them for 20 minutes until they are golden brown.

4

5 When your birthday cupcakes are cool, mix 100g of icing sugar with a little water and add a drop of colouring. Spread some icing over each cake and then decorate with...

5

silver balls

sugar flowers

chocolate drops

love hearts

hundreds and thousands

Don't forget to make a wish when you blow out the candles on your birthday! This is the one day of the year when every human is given a secret helping of Rainbow Magic to make their dreams come true!

Hidden Gems Wordsearch

Now jealous Jack Frost has stolen the jewels from Queen Titania's crown! Can you find the seven Jewel Fairies and their jewels in this wordsearch grid? The words could be hiding forwards, backwards, diagonally or even upside down.

F	L	C	E	R	I	H	P	P	A	S
A	E	H	Q	K	T	B	I	B	P	T
M	C	L	A	M	E	J	Y	E	Z	J
E	N	O	T	S	N	O	O	M	H	L
T	V	E	N	D	R	E	Q	I	A	U
H	S	T	O	P	A	Z	N	L	E	C
Y	M	F	H	K	G	L	X	Y	I	Y
S	C	A	R	L	E	T	T	U	H	O
T	W	I	N	D	I	A	R	C	P	I
G	E	M	E	R	A	L	D	Y	O	A
U	D	D	N	O	M	A	I	D	S	G

AMY, AMETHYST

EMILY, EMERALD

SOPHIE, SAPPHIRE

SCARLETT, GARNET

INDIA, MOONSTONE

CHLOE, TOPAZ

LUCY, DIAMOND

50

Answers can be found on page 61!

Meet Izzy the Indigo Fairy

Izzy the Indigo Fairy has brilliant purple eyes and a silver-tipped wand that showers fairy dust inkdrops!

Before Kirsty and Rachel rescued me, I thought I might be trapped forever in the pages of a storybook!

Personality
Wise, calm and glowing with magic!

Happiest hobby
Sunset spotting. Izzy loves to find somewhere quiet to sit and watch the daily magic of the sun going down.

Favourite colour
Deep purple, the colour of magic and wonder.

Fairy playmates
The Fun Day Fairies.

Yummiest food
Blackcurrant jelly beans and juicy grapes.

Izzy is the most mystical of the Rainbow sisters and can always come up with a magical solution to any problem!

Fairy outfit
Izzy combs her blue-black bob so that it shines beautifully next to her dark denim jacket and jeans. Tiny fairy fingers have stitched spangly patches all over her outfit!

The Land of Sweets

Now that they had discovered five tiny Rainbow Magic sisters, Kirsty and Rachel were experts at finding fairies! Instead of hunting high and low all over Rainspell Island, Queen Titania had taught them to let the magic find its way to them. One rainy afternoon the girls decided to read a storybook while they waited…

"I know this story," said Rachel. "It's called *The Nutcracker.*" Kirsty gazed at the picture on the page of snowflakes swirling through a forest.

"The snow looks so real," she said. Rachel put out her hand and touched the paper. It felt cold and wet.

"It is real!" she gasped.

Kirsty looked down at the book again. The snowflakes started to swirl up from the pages, out into the bedroom.

The friends soon found themselves being swept up into the air by the spinning snow cloud. Suddenly the snowflakes stopped swirling. Rachel and Kirsty were now standing in a forest, with their rucksacks at their feet.

"We're inside the book!" said Kirsty. She bent and touched a snowdrift. "This isn't snow," she laughed. "It's icing sugar!"

"Wait," whispered Rachel. "I just heard voices!"

"Goblins?" Kirsty whispered back, looking scared.

Kirsty and Rachel peered through the trees. In front of them two people wearing fluffy white coats were scooping icing sugar into shiny metal buckets.

"I think they're elves," Kirsty whispered. "But they're the same size as we are. That means we must be fairy-sized, or at least elf-sized, again."

"But we haven't got any wings this time," Rachel pointed out.

Suddenly one of the elves spotted them. "Hello!" she called. "Welcome to the Land of Sweets."

"My name is Wafer," said the elf. "And this is my sister, Cornet."

"We're the ice-cream makers," added Cornet. "What are you doing here?"

When Rachel and Kirsty explained their search, the elves were happy to help. They led the pair through an archway of sweets. On the other side the sun shone warmly. Flowers made of strawberry cream grew beneath milk-chocolate trees. Pink and white marshmallow houses lined the street, which was paved with boiled sweets.

"Isn't this great?" Kirsty laughed. "It's like being inside a giant sweet shop!"

A small elf ran towards them, one hand clapped over his mouth.

"That's our little brother, Scoop," Wafer explained.

Laughing, Scoop took his hands away from his mouth. His lips were indigo!

"I had a drink from the lemonade fountain," he giggled. "All the lemonade's turned bluey-purple. It made my tongue tingle, too!"

Rachel grabbed Kirsty's arm.

"We've found Izzy!"

You can read more about this adventure in *Izzy the Indigo Fairy* (see pages 62/63 for details).

Fairy Friendship Necklace

Phoebe the Fashion Fairy has designed this stunning pendant make-it for you to share with your best friend. Follow the easy steps to create two original handmade necklaces – one for each of you to treasure forever!

First collect...

Baking sheet
Silver foil
Non-toxic modelling clay
Cocktail sticks
Rolling pin
Small heart-shaped cookie cutter

Old newspapers
Acrylic paints
Paintbrushes
Large blunt needle
Thin ribbon
Scissors

1 Ask a grown-up to pre-heat the oven to 130°C/250°F/Gas Mark 1. Line a baking sheet with silver foil and put it to one side.

2 Pull off a small lump of clay and knead it gently with your fingers to soften it up.

3 When the clay becomes easy to shape, roll out 12 marble-sized balls. These will become your fairy beads.

4 Carefully push a cocktail stick through each bead to make a hole large enough for a ribbon to be threaded through later. Place your beads on the baking sheet.

5 Roll out a piece of clay approx 2cm thick then gently push a small heart-shaped cookie cutter into it twice to make two pendants.

6 Carefully push the cocktail stick through each heart to make a good-sized ribbon-hole. Keep the hole near the top so the pendants won't turn over on the ribbon when they are worn.

7 Add the hearts to the foil-lined tray and ask an adult to pop this in the oven for 25 minutes.

8 When the baked clay pieces have cooled completely, place them on some old newspapers. Paint both hearts one colour and the beads in a variety of pretty colours. You will need to paint the pieces in stages so that they get completely covered with colour. Leave everything to dry overnight. The next morning, paint your name on one heart and the name of your best friend on the other heart, using a thin paintbrush.

9 Thread the needle with a length of coloured ribbon, then thread 3 beads through in alternate colours. Now add one of the heart pendants and 3 more beads.

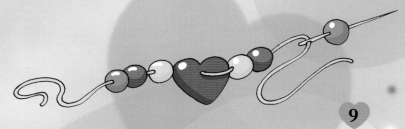

10 Take the other piece of ribbon and make up the second heart necklace in the same way.

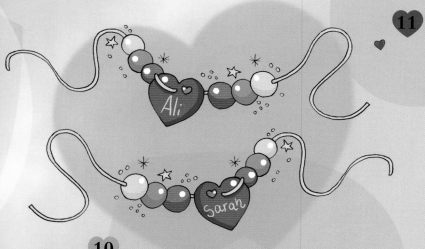

11 Give your best friend the necklace with your name on it, tying the ribbon at the back with a bow. Now ask her to help you put on the pendant with her name on it so that everyone knows you are friends forever!

Make a fairy promise to wear your necklaces every week!

Why not try...

Making a totally unique thumbprint pendant, by pressing each other's thumbprint into the back of the heart shapes before they are baked in the oven?

Perfect Pets

The Pet Keeper Fairies love their animals more than anything else in the world. Now they've each brought an adorable little friend to say hello to you!

Penny the Pony Fairy

Penny is best friends with her pony, Glitter. Glitter is a miniature, sparkling pony with the shiniest white coat ever. If Penny needs to escape from goblins, she and Glitter will gallop up into the sky.

Katie the Kitten Fairy

Katie has the sweetest kitten, called Shimmer! Shimmer is white with grey patches on her tail, face and paws. If a dog comes near, the kitten uses her magic to transform into a fierce tiger! Shimmer's favourite food is fish fingers.

Lauren the Puppy Fairy

Lauren can't resist her puppy's beautiful big brown eyes! Sunny is a sandy Springer Spaniel. His name is engraved in glittering blue letters on a bone-shaped name tag on his collar. As he is a magic puppy, Sunny can make rubber balls appear out of thin air!

Georgia the Guinea Pig Fairy

Georgia's guinea pig Sparky is a very special little fellow! The orange and white pet talks to his fairy owner in a ripple of squeaks that only she can understand. If Georgia offers him a carrot to nibble, Sparky's face lights up with a whiskery smile.

Harriet the Hamster Fairy

Harriet is devoted to her tiny hamster, Twinkle! The friendly creature has apricot and white fur and the brightest eyes. When Twinkle wrinkles her little nose, dazzling showers of glittering red sparkles appear! The hamster loves spinning on her wheel.

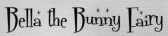

Bella the Bunny Fairy

Bella's fluffy baby bunny is called Misty. The hoppy little creature normally has brown and white patches, but she can change colours with just a twitch of her nose! When Kirsty and Rachel first saw her, Misty had turned a beautiful shade of lilac.

Molly the Goldfish Fairy

Molly's adorable little goldfish is called Flash. He has dazzling gold fins that seem to shimmer as he swims through the water. Whenever Molly puts her fingers in his bowl, the loyal pet floats up to talk to her in shiny rainbow-coloured air bubbles.

Meet Heather
the Violet Fairy

When Heather the Violet Fairy was reunited with all her sisters, the colour could finally be put back into Fairyland!

I was in a spin on a carousel when Kirsty and Rachel set me free!

Personality
Graceful, merry and bursting with music!

Happiest hobby
Heather loves to make music. She spends hours writing sweet fairy songs or trying to learn a new instrument.

Favourite colour
Violet, the colour of music and melody.

Fairy playmates
The Party Fairies and the Dance Fairies.

Yummiest food
Sweet parma violets and dewberry fruit smoothies.

Heather is always finding new ways to entertain her friends. Her tinkly singing voice makes her sisters smile!

Fairy outfit
The most beautiful scent of violet blossom follows Heather into every room. Heather likes to wear her short empire-line dress with mauve socks and ballet pumps. She wears a string of pretty beads around her neck.

The Magic
Rainbow Bubble

As soon as Kirsty and Rachel had set Heather free, they took the little Violet Fairy to meet her sisters at the pot at the end of the rainbow. The Rainbow Fairies were so thrilled to be together again, the air fizzed with scented bubbles, flowers and leaves, stars, ink drops and tiny butterflies! But when it suddenly turned icy, the friends realised that their troubles weren't over yet…

A tall, bony figure walked into the fairy glade. Jack Frost!

"So, you are all together again!" His voice sounded like icicles snapping.

"Yes, thanks to Kirsty and Rachel," Ruby declared bravely. "And now we want to go home to Fairyland!"

Izzy shot to her sister's side, followed by the other fairies. They all lifted their wands and chanted:

*"To protect the Rainbow Fairies all,
Make a magic raindrop wall!"*

Suddenly a shining wall of raindrops appeared between the fairies and Jack Frost.

"It will take more than a few raindrops to stop me!" Jack Frost hissed. He pointed a bony finger at the shimmering wall.

The raindrops turned to ice. They dropped onto the frosty grass like tiny glass beads and shattered.

Saffron and Sky gave a sob of dismay and Izzy clenched her fists. Fern, Ruby and Amber hugged each other. Heather looked as if she was thinking hard. Then she waved her wand and cried:

*"To stop Jack Frost
from causing trouble,
Catch him in a magic bubble!"*

A gleaming bubble popped out from the end of Heather's wand. It grew bigger and bigger. Jack Frost laughed and stretched out his icy fingers. But before he could do anything, there was a loud fizzing sound.

Rachel blinked in surprise.

Heather's spell had trapped Jack Frost inside the bubble! The wicked creature pressed his hands against the pale lilac wall, looking furious.

"Well done, Heather!" Fern exclaimed. "That was very brave."

"Quick, everyone. We must get into the pot at the end of the rainbow and magic a rainbow to take us back to Fairyland," Heather urged.

The Violet Fairy fluttered in front of Rachel and Kirsty.

"Would you like to come to Fairyland with us?"

Rachel and Kirsty nodded. Heather waved her wand, sprinkling the girls with purple fairy dust.

Kirsty felt herself shrinking.

"Hurrah! I'm a fairy again!" she cried.

You can read more about this adventure in *Heather the Violet Fairy* (see pages 62/63 for details).

Fairy Farewell

Here's a special place to collect together the ten objects that the naughty goblins tried to steal. Draw the fairy things here and write their names next to each one.

_____ _____

_____ _____

_____ _____

_____ _____

_____ _____

Now write down the first letter from each stolen object in the spaces below. If you can unjumble them you'll discover that the letters spell out the thing that Rainbow Fairies prize more than anything else in Fairyland!

_ _ _ _ _ _ _ _ _ _

I'll be back next time!

What a clever fairy friend you are, well done! Thank you for stopping Jack Frost's mischievous troupe of goblins. We have so enjoyed sharing our magic annual with you. Will you come and share some adventures with us again soon?

Keep believing in Fairies!

All our love,

Ruby, Amber, Saffron, Fern, Sky, Izzy and Heather
x x x x x x

Answers

Page 14
Days Maze

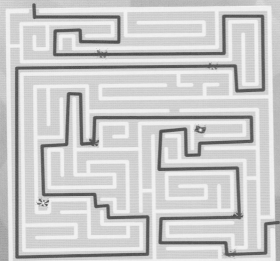

Page 21
Bertram's Big Crossword

	¹M							⁴F
¹R	A	I	N	S	P	E	L	L
	G							Y
²T	I	T	A	N	I	A		
	C			²C				
	B		³S	W	E	E	T	S
	A							
	G		³C					
⁴S	A	F	F	R	O	N		
			A					
		⁵B	E	A	D	S		

Page 39
Magical Mottos

1. Friends forever.
2. Smiles and hugs for you.
3. Dreams do come true.

Page 50
Hidden Gems Wordsearch

F	L	C	E	R	I	H	P	P	A	S
A	E	H	Q	K	T	B	I	B	P	T
M	C	L	A	M	E	J	Y	E	Z	J
E	N	O	T	S	N	O	O	M	H	L
T	V	E	N	D	R	E	Q	I	A	U
H	S	T	O	P	A	Z	N	L	E	C
Y	M	F	H	K	G	L	X	Y	I	Y
S	C	A	R	L	E	T	T	U	H	O
T	W	I	N	D	I	A	R	C	P	I
G	E	M	E	R	A	L	D	Y	O	A
U	D	D	N	O	M	A	I	D	S	G

Objects stolen by the naughty goblins…

pg 13 - Flower
pg 21 - Star
pg 25 - Rainbow
pg 27 - Needle
pg 28 - Ice cube
pg 34 - Invite
pg 41 - Purse
pg 47 - Hairbrush
pg 48 - Egg
pg 50 - Diamond

When rearranged, the first letters of the above words show us that the Rainbow Fairies value friendship more than anything else!

Meet all the Rainbow Magic fairies in these exciting storybooks!

The Rainbow Fairies

Ruby the Red Fairy	Amber the Orange Fairy	Saffron the Yellow Fairy	Fern the Green Fairy	Sky the Blue Fairy	Izzy the Indigo Fairy	Heather the Violet Fairy
978-1-84362-0167	978-1-84362-0174	978-1-84362-0181	978-1-84362-0198	978-1-84362-0204	978-1-84362-0211	978-1-84362-0228

The Weather Fairies

Crystal the Snow Fairy	Abigail the Breeze Fairy	Pearl the Cloud Fairy	Goldie the Sunshine Fairy	Evie the Mist Fairy	Storm the Lightning Fairy	Hayley the Rain Fairy
978-1-84362-6336	978-1-84362-6343	978-1-84362-6350	978-1-84362-6411	978-1-84362-6367	978-1-84362-6374	978-1-84362-6381

The Party Fairies

Cherry the Cake Fairy	Melodie the Music Fairy	Grace the Glitter Fairy	Honey the Sweet Fairy	Polly the Party Fun Fairy	Phoebe the Fashion Fairy	Jasmine the Present Fairy
978-1-84362-8187	978-1-84362-8194	978-1-84362-8200	978-1-84362-8217	978-1-84362-8224	978-1-84362-8231	978-1-84362-8248

The Jewel Fairies

India the Moonstone Fairy	Scarlett the Garnet Fairy	Emily the Emerald Fairy	Chloe the Topaz Fairy	Amy the Amethyst Fairy	Sophie the Sapphire Fairy	Lucy the Diamond Fairy
978-1-84362-9580	978-1-84362-9542	978-1-84362-9559	978-1-84362-9566	978-1-84362-9573	978-1-84362-9535	978-1-84362-9597

The Pet Keeper Fairies

Katie the Kitten Fairy	Bella the Bunny Fairy	Georgia the Guinea Pig Fairy	Lauren the Puppy Fairy	Harriet the Hamster Fairy	Molly the Goldfish Fairy	Penny the Pony Fairy
978-1-84616-1667	978-1-84616-1704	978-1-84616-1681	978-1-84616-1698	978-1-84616-1674	978-1-84616-1728	978-1-84616-1711

The Fun Day Fairies

Megan the Monday Fairy	Tallulah the Tuesday Fairy	Willow the Wednesday Fairy	Thea the Thursday Fairy	Freya the Friday Fairy	Sienna the Saturday Fairy	Sarah the Sunday Fairy
978-1-84616-1889	978-1-84616-1896	978-1-84616-1902	978-1-84616-1919	978-1-84616-1926	978-1-84616-1933	978-1-84616-1940